SFX-3
BEATLES HIT

All You Need Is Love 4
And I Love Her 24
Can't Buy Me Love 14
Day Tripper 22
Eleanor Rigby 34
The Fool On The Hill 7
Get Back 32
A Hard Day's Night 26
Hey Jude 36
I Feel Fine 40
I Want To Hold Your Hand 12
I'll Follow The Sun 28
Let It Be 10
Michelle 38
Norwegian Wood 42
Nowhere Man 30
Ob-La-Di, Ob-La-Da 18
We Can Work It Out 45
Yesterday 16

The ABC Of SFX 2
MASTER CHORD CHART 48

FOR ALL HOME
SFX
KEYBOARDS

Exclusive Distributors:
Music Sales Limited
8/9 Frith Street, London W1V 5TZ, England.
Music Sales Pty Limited
120 Rothschild Avenue, Rosebery, NSW 2018, Australia.

This book © Copyright 1983, 1992 by Wise Publications
Order No.AM33093
ISBN 0-7119-0302-6

Designed by Pearce Marchbank Studio

Music Sales' complete catalogue lists thousands of titles and is
free from your local music shop, or direct from Music Sales Limited.
Please send a cheque/postal order for £1.50 for postage to
Music Sales Limited, Newmarket Road, Bury St. Edmunds, Suffolk IP33 3YB.

Your Guarantee of Quality
As publishers, we strive to produce every book to the highest
commercial standards.
The book has been carefully designed to minimise awkward page turns,
and to make playing from it a real pleasure.
Particular care has been given to specifying acid-free, neutral-sized
paper which has not been chlorine bleached but produced with
special regard for the environment. Throughout, the printing and
binding have been planned to ensure a sturdy, attractive
publication which should give years of enjoyment.
If your copy fails to meet our high standards, please inform us and
we will gladly replace it.

Wise Publications
London/New York/Sydney

The ABC of SFX Music

In SFX music, the melody is clearly written in large lettered notes. Each note can easily be located on your keyboard and then played with the right hand.

The songs in SFX music books are all written in the following keyboard range. The symbol at the beginning of the music staff is the treble clef, indicating the notes are played with the right hand:

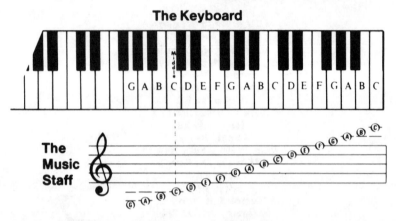

The Sharp Sign (♯) will sometimes appear before a music note. Simply play the *black key* to the *right* of the *white key:*

The Flat Sign (♭) placed before a note tells you to play the *black key* that lies to the *left* of the *white key:*

The Music Staff is divided into equal sections by vertical lines called *Bar Lines.* Each section is a *Measure.* The end of a piece of music is marked by a double bar line.

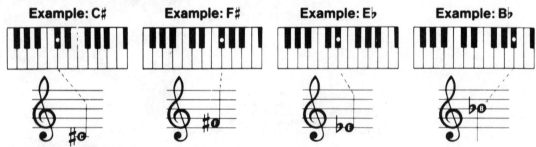

All music is played in time to a *beat.* The six types of notes most often used in SFX music all have a *time value* that relates to the beat:

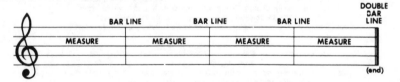

Whole note	Dotted half note	Half note	Dotted quarter note	Quarter note	Eighth note
4 Beats	3 Beats	2 Beats	1½ Beats	1 Beat	½ Beat

The Rest is a silent break in the music. The symbols are written in the staff, and like music notes, rests each have a time value:

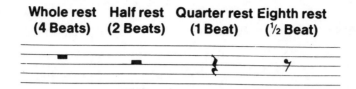

Whole rest | **Half rest** | **Quarter rest** | **Eighth rest**
(4 Beats) | (2 Beats) | (1 Beat) | (½ Beat)

The Time Signature comprises two numbers at the beginning of the music, after the treble clef sign. The top number shows the amount of beats in each measure. The bottom number indicates the type of note that will receive *one* beat. These are the most popular time signatures. The lower number 4 represents the quarter note:

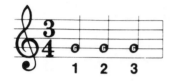

The Tie is a curved line that connects two consecutive notes on the same line or in the same space in the staff. When a tie appears in the music, play the first note and sustain the sound for the *total* time value of the two notes:

Tied Notes

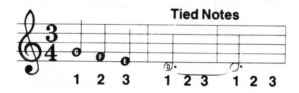

Repeat Signs are two dots alongside double bar lines. They indicate that all the music in between the pairs of repeat signs is to be played through again:

Quite often there will only be one repeat sign at the end of a passage of music. The repeat is then made from the very beginning:

Double Endings are sections of music with staff repeat signs. 1st and 2nd time brackets above the staff indicate where a short 'skip' is to be made in the music after the repeat has been played:

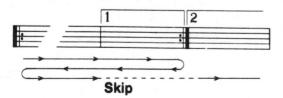

Skip

Left Hand Keyboard Accompaniment. SFX music has Major and Minor chords clearly written above the staff. The optional 'seventh' type of chord is shown with the 7 outside the chord frame:

Your keyboard Owner's Manual will explain how these chords are played with your left hand.

Conventional (Fingered) Chords can also be used. **The SFX Master Chord Chart** in this book shows the most practical chord positions for this type of left hand accompaniment.

All You Need Is Love

Suggested Registration:
PIANO or GUITAR
Rhythm: ROCK
Tempo: MEDIUM

Words and Music by
John Lennon & Paul McCartney

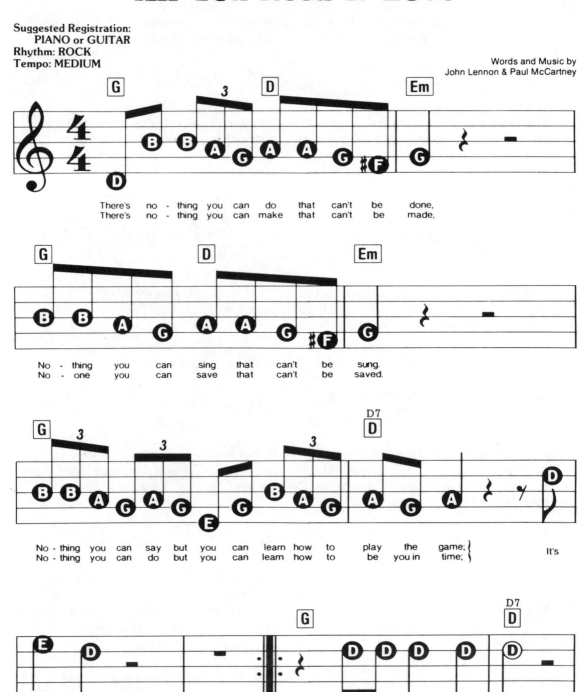

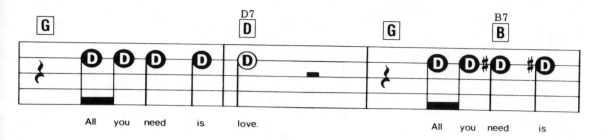

All you need is love.　　　　All you need is

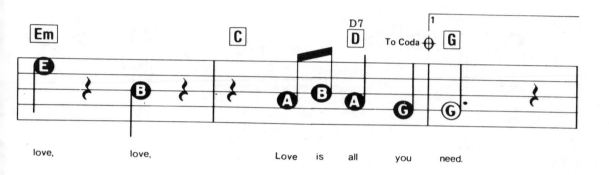

love,　　love,　　Love is all you need.

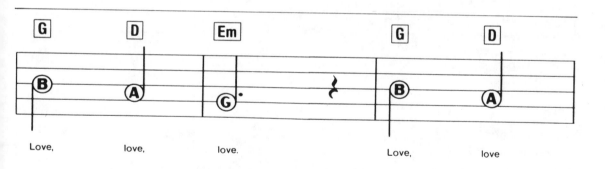

Love,　　love,　　love.　　　　Love,　　love

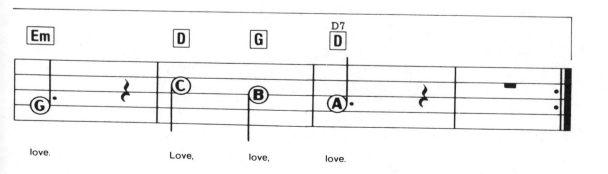

love.　　Love,　　love,　　love.

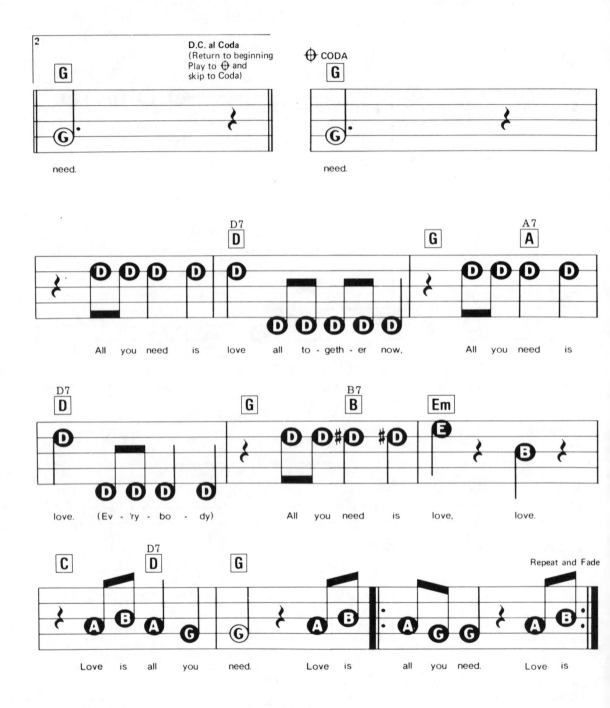

VERSE 3: There's nothing you can know that isn't known,
Nothing you can see that isn't shown.
Nowhere you can be that isn't where you're meant to be;
It's easy.

The Fool On The Hill

Suggested Registration:
OBOE or VIBRAPHONE
Rhythm: WALTZ & SOFT ROCK
Tempo: MEDIUM SLOW

By John Lennon
and Paul McCartney

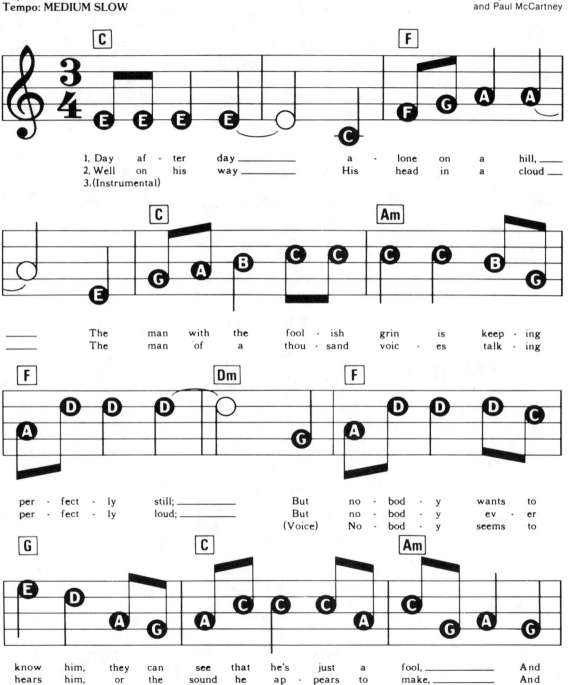

1, Day af - ter day _____ a - lone on a hill, _____
2, Well on his way _____ His head in a cloud _____
3,(Instrumental)

_____ The man with the fool - ish grin is keep - ing
The man of a thou - sand voic - es talk - ing

per - fect - ly still; _____ But no - bod - y wants to
per - fect - ly loud; _____ But no - bod - y ev - er
(Voice) No - bod - y seems to

know him, they can see that he's just a fool, _____ And
hears him, or the sound he ap - pears to make, _____ And
like him they can tell what he wants to do, _____ And

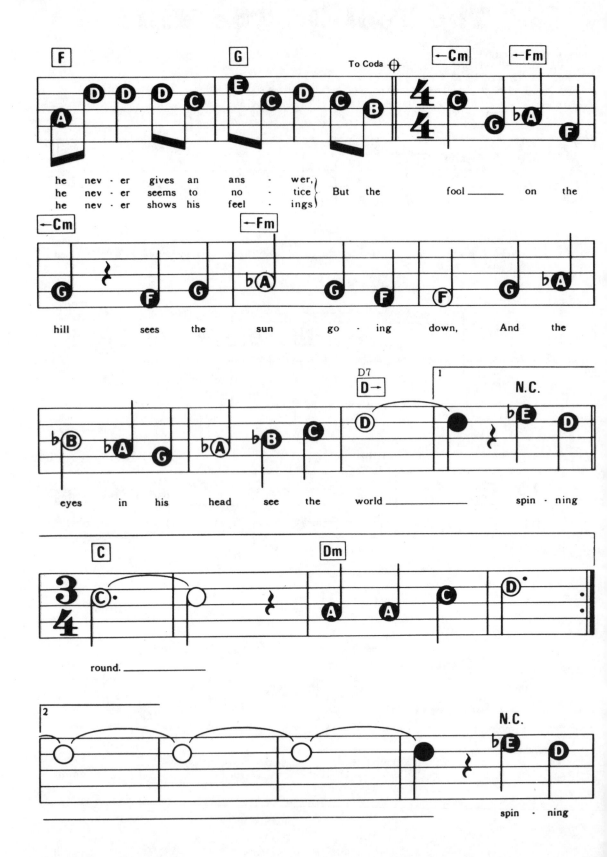

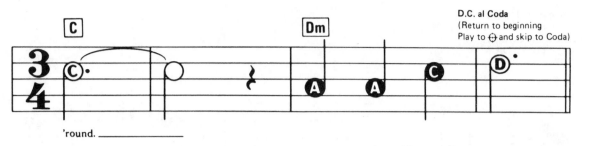

'round. _____

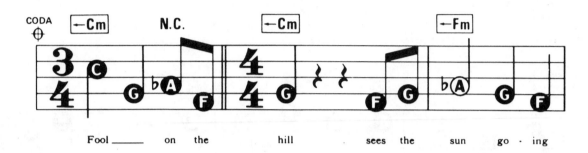

Fool _____ on the hill sees the sun go · ing

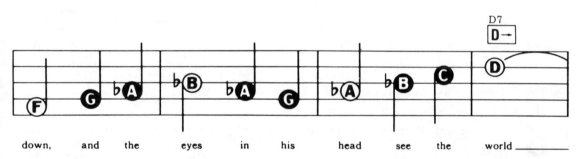

down, and the eyes in his head see the world _____

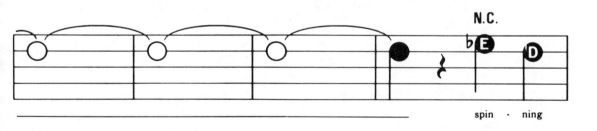

spin - ning

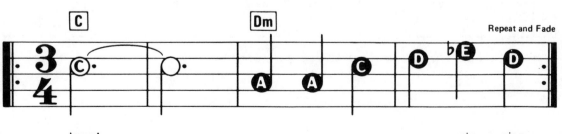

'round. _____ spin · ning

Let It Be

Suggested Registration:
FLUTE or VIBRAPHONE
Rhythm: SOFT ROCK
Tempo: MEDIUM

Words and Music by John Lennon &
Paul McCartney

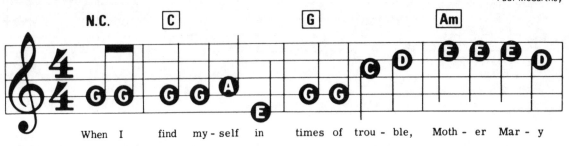

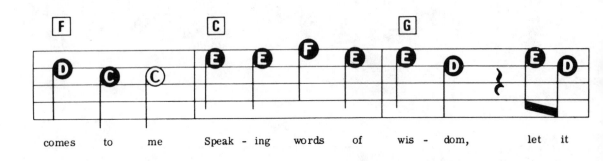

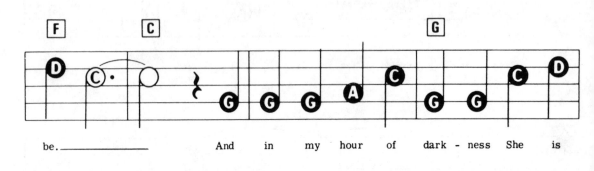

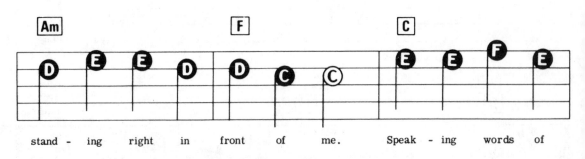

11

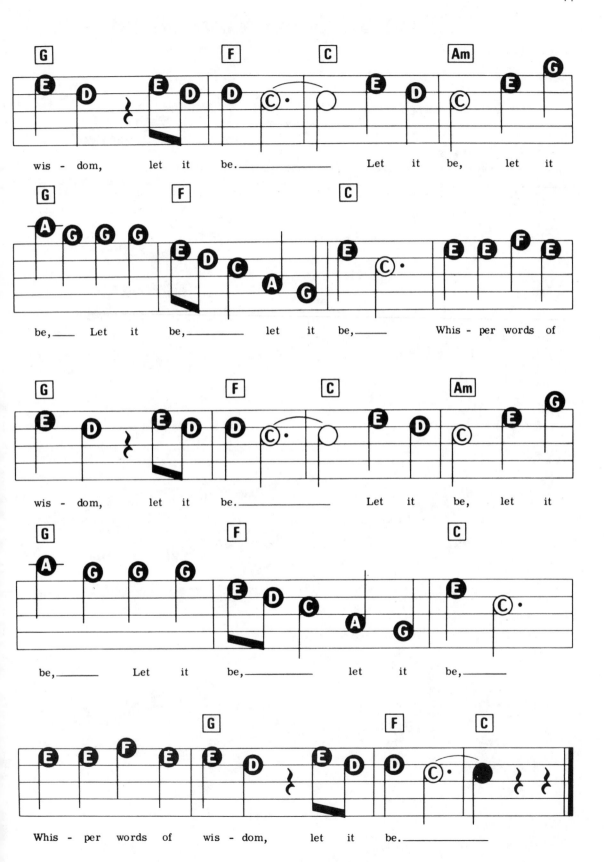

I Want To Hold Your Hand

Suggested Registration:
 JAZZ ORGAN or GUITAR
Rhythm: ROCK
Tempo: MEDIUM

Words and Music by John Lennon &
Paul McCartney

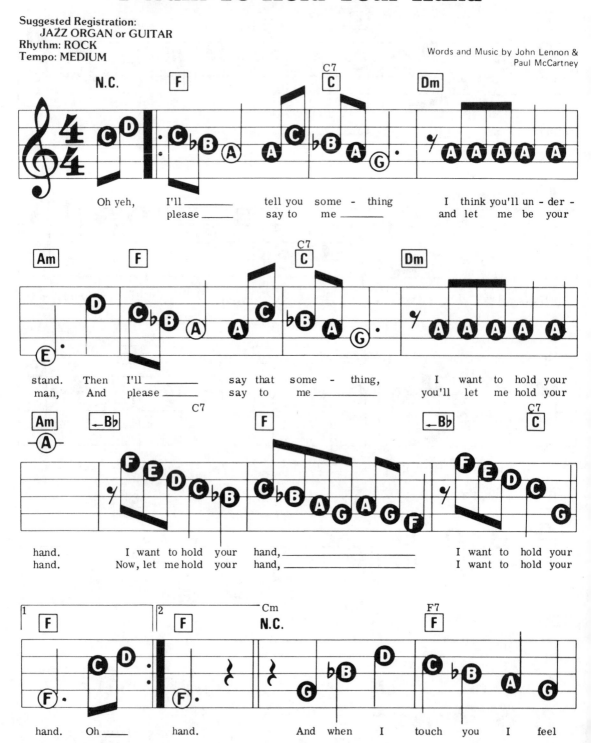

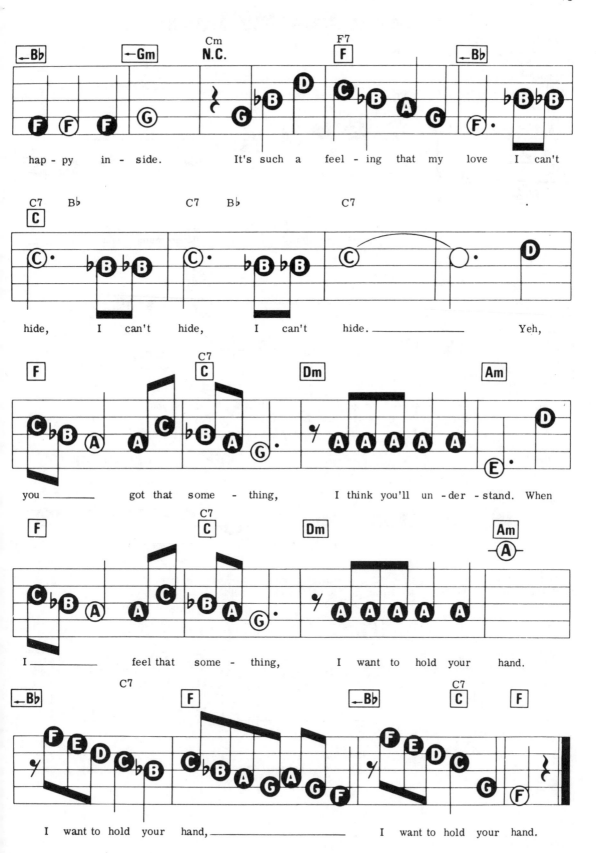

Can't Buy Me Love

Suggested Registration:
VIBRAPHONE or JAZZ ORGAN
Rhythm: SWING
Tempo: MEDIUM FAST

Words and Music by John Lennon &
Paul McCartney

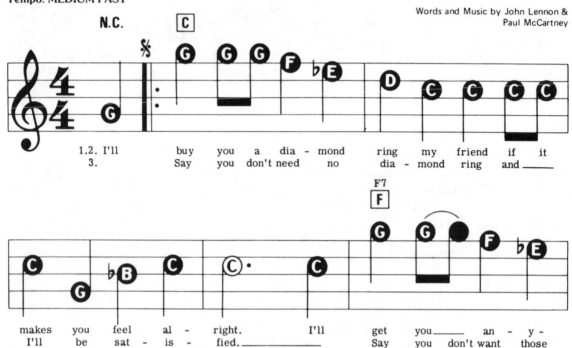

1.2. I'll buy you a dia - mond ring my friend if it
3. Say you don't need no dia - mond ring and _____

makes you feel al - right. I'll get you_____ an - y -
I'll be sat - is - fied._____ Say you don't want those

thing my friend if it makes you feel al - right. For
kind of things that _____ mon - ey just can't buy. For

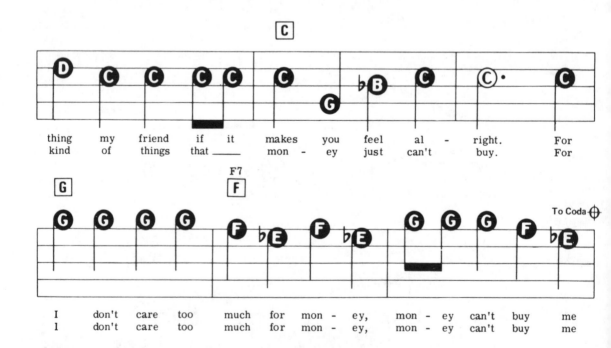

I don't care too much for mon - ey, mon - ey can't buy me
I don't care too much for mon - ey, mon - ey can't buy me

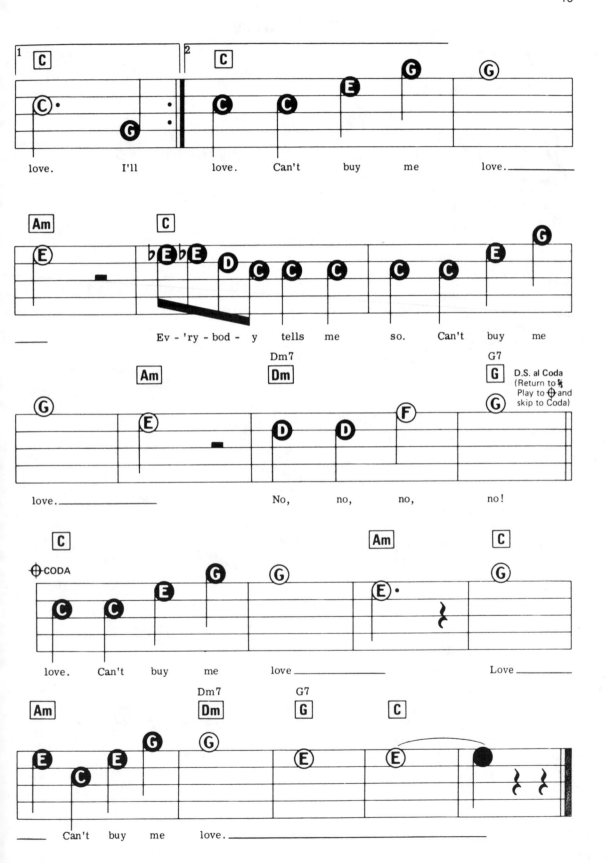

Yesterday

Suggested Registration:
STRINGS or FLUTE
Rhythm: SOFT ROCK
Tempo: MEDIUM SLOW

Words and Music by John Lennon &
Paul McCartney

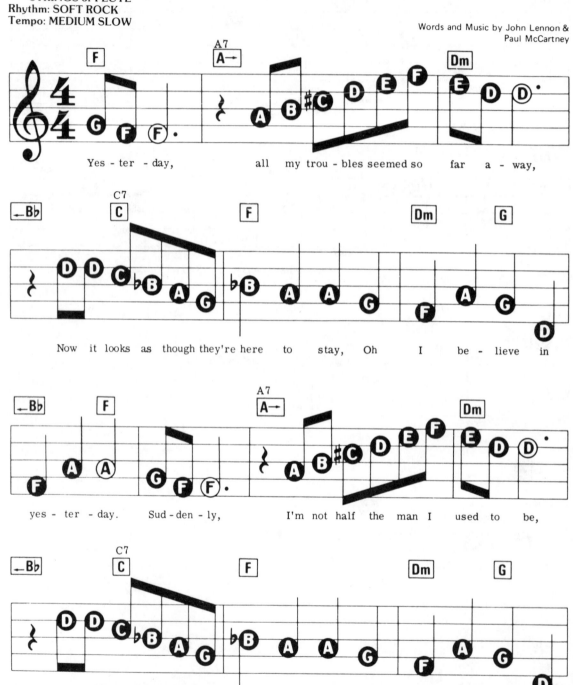

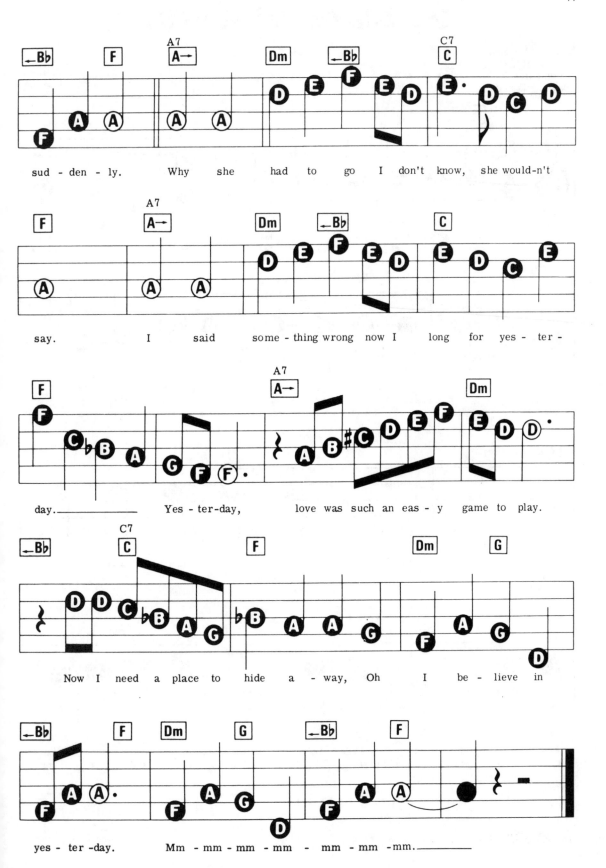

Ob-La-Di, Ob-La-Da

Suggested Registration:
   TRUMPET or JAZZ ORGAN
Rhythm: ROCK
Tempo: MEDIUM

Words and Music by John Lennon
and Paul McCartney

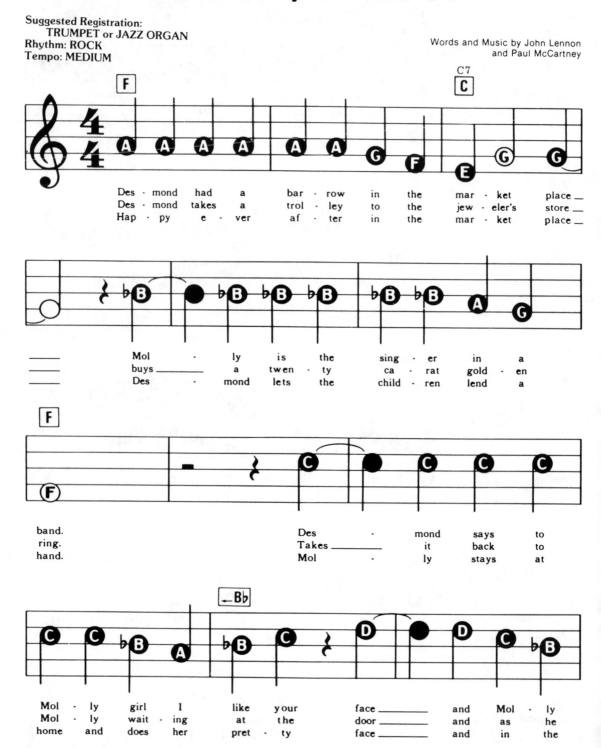

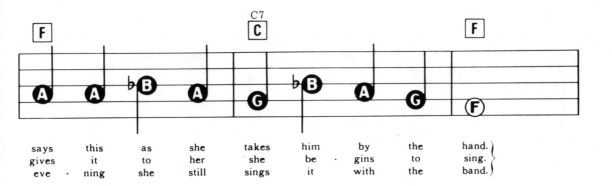

says	this	as	she	takes	him	by	the	hand.
gives	it	to	her	she	be -	gins	to	sing.
eve -	ning	to she	her still	sings	it	with	the	band.

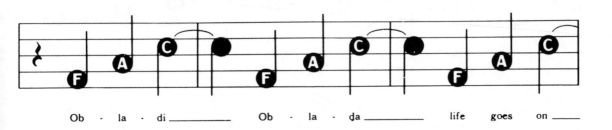

Ob - la - di _____ Ob - la - da _____ life goes on _____

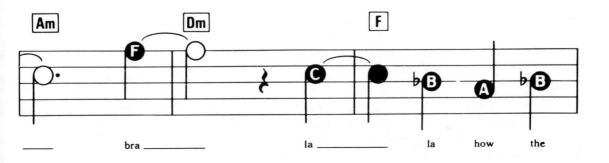

_____ bra _____ la _____ la how the

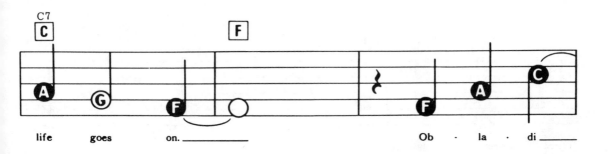

life goes on. _____ Ob - la - di _____

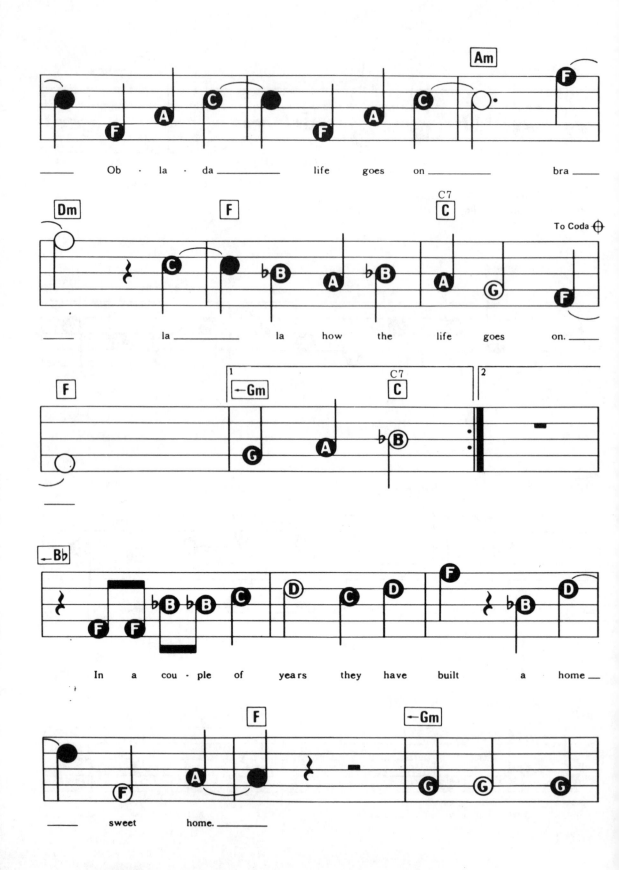

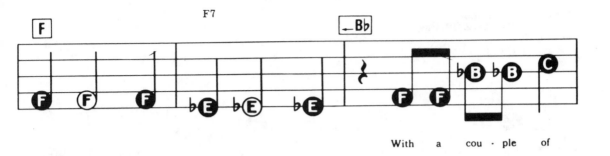

With a cou-ple of

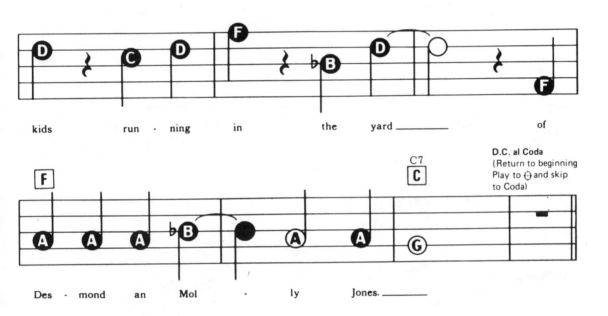

kids run - ning in the yard _____ of

F

C7
C

D.C. al Coda
(Return to beginning
Play to ⊕ and skip
to Coda)

Des - mond an Mol - ly Jones. _____

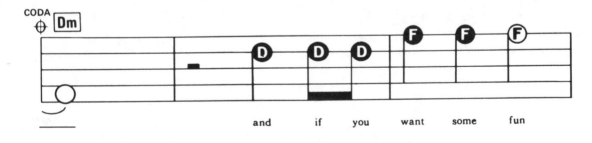

CODA

and if you want some fun

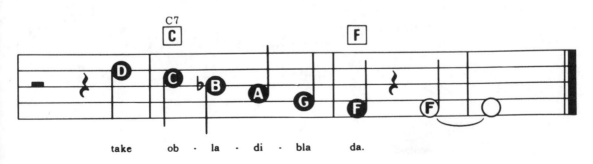

take ob - la - di - bla - da.

Day Tripper

Suggested Registration:
GUITAR or JAZZ ORGAN
Rhythm: ROCK
Tempo: MEDIUM

Words and Music by
John Lennon and Paul McCartney

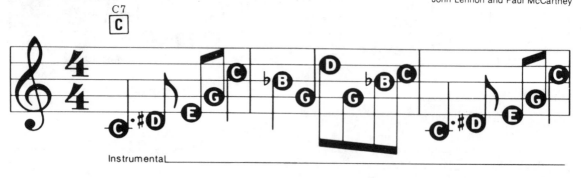

Instrumental

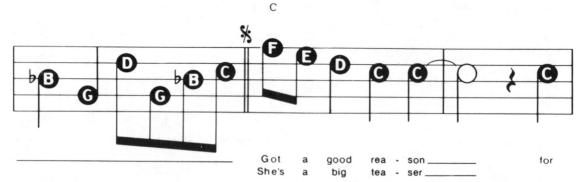

Got a good rea - son _____ for
She's a big tea - ser _____

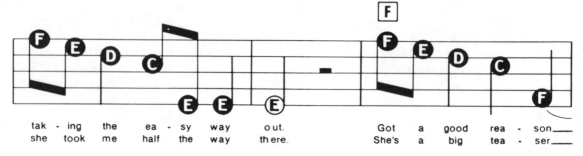

tak - ing the ea - sy way out.
she took me half the way there.
Got a good rea - son ____
She's a big tea - ser ____

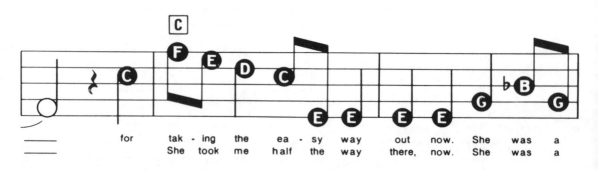

for tak - ing the ea - sy way out now. She was a
She took me half the way there, now. She was a

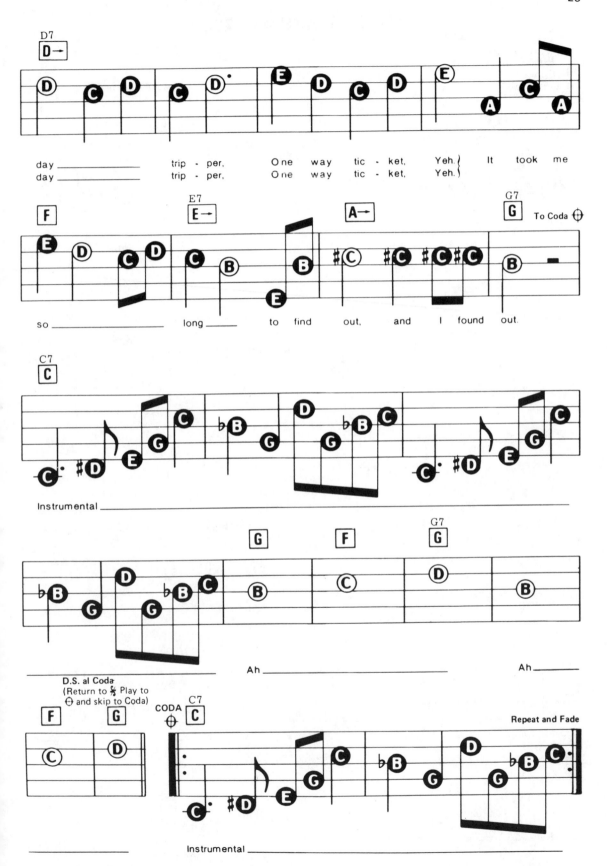

And I Love Her

Suggested Registration:
PIANO or GUITAR
Rhythm: LATIN
Tempo: MEDIUM

Words and Music by John Lennon &
Paul McCartney

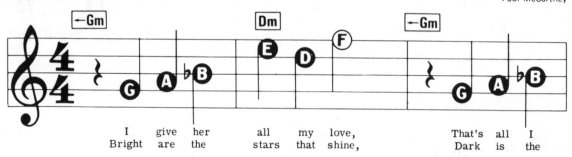

I give her all my love,
Bright are the stars that shine,
That's all I
Dark is the

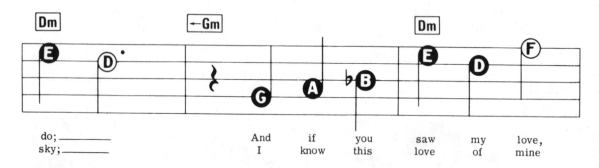

do; _____
sky; _____
And if you saw my love,
I know this love of mine

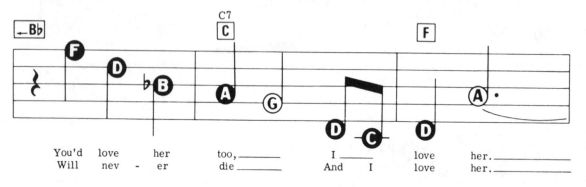

You'd love her too, _____
Will nev - er die _____
I _____ love her. _____
And I love her. _____

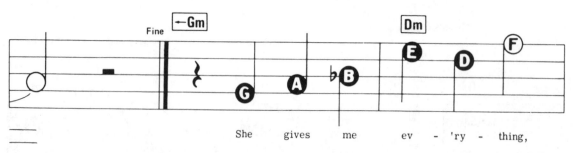

Fine

She gives me ev - 'ry - thing,

25

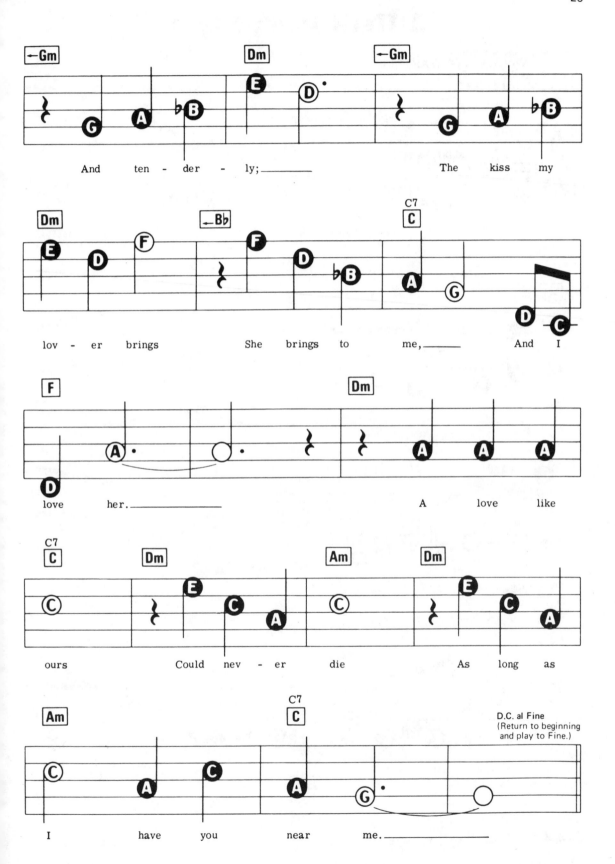

A Hard Day's Night

Suggested Registration:
 JAZZ ORGAN or GUITAR
Rhythm: ROCK
Tempo: MEDIUM FAST

Words and Music by John Lennon &
Paul McCartney

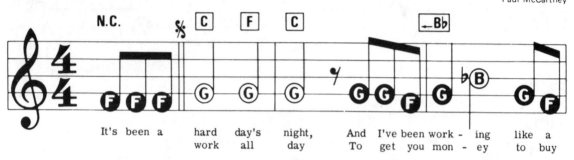

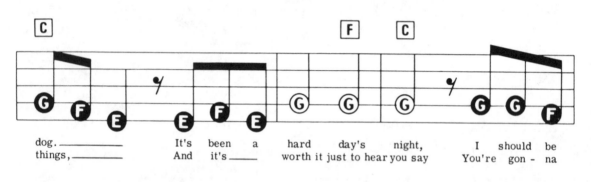

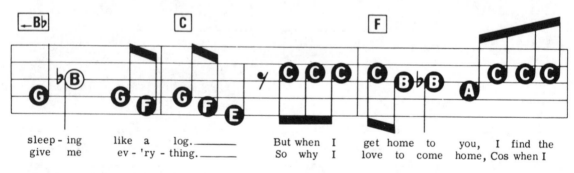

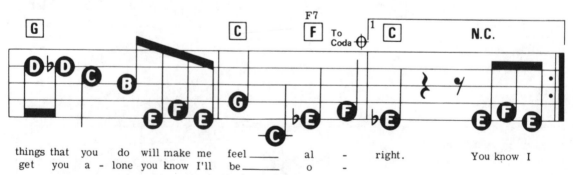

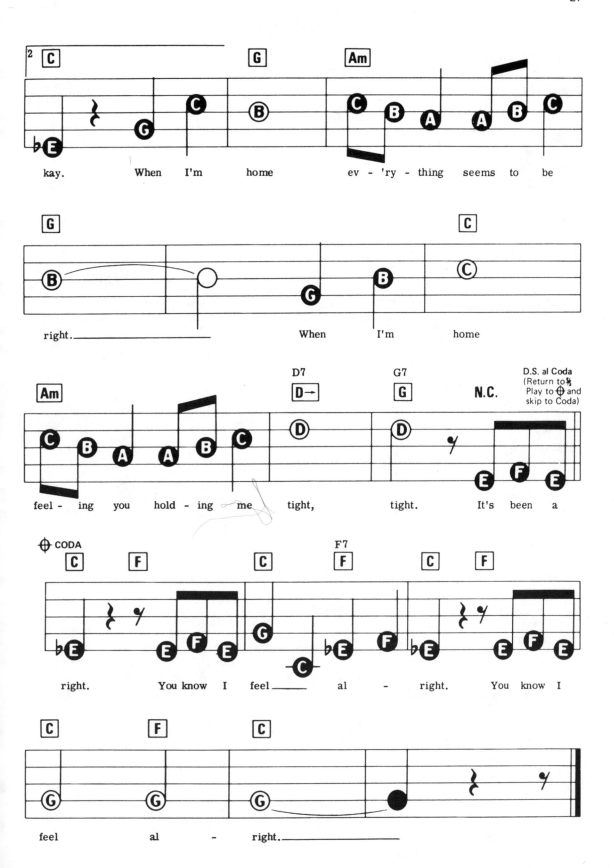

I'll Follow The Sun

Suggested Registration:
PIANO or VIBRAPHONE
Rhythm: SOFT ROCK
Tempo: MEDIUM

Words and Music by John Lennon &
Paul McCartney

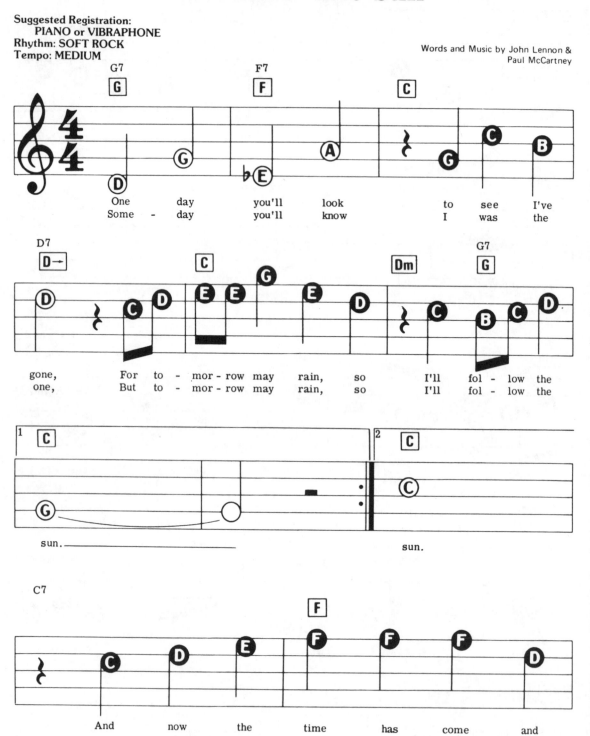

29

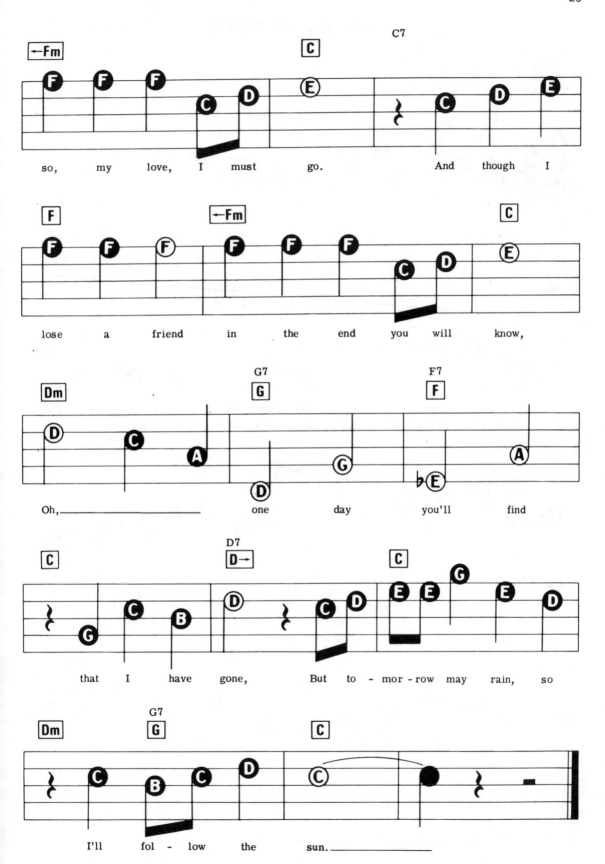

Nowhere Man

Suggested Registration:
PIANO or VIBRAPHONE
Rhythm: SOFT ROCK
Tempo: MEDIUM

Words and Music by John Lennon &
Paul McCartney

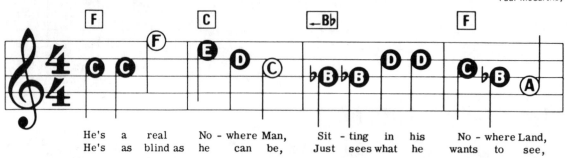

He's a real No - where Man, Sit - ting in his No - where Land,
He's as blind as he can be, Just sees what he wants to see,

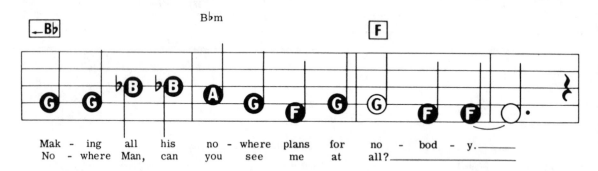

Mak - ing all his no - where plans for no - bod - y._____
No - where Man, can you see me at all?_____

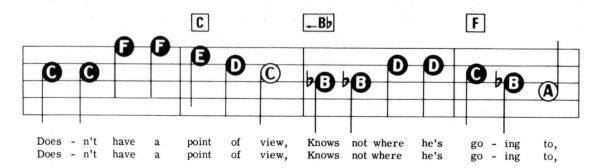

Does - n't have a point of view, Knows not where he's go - ing to,
Does - n't have a point of view, Knows not where he's go - ing to,

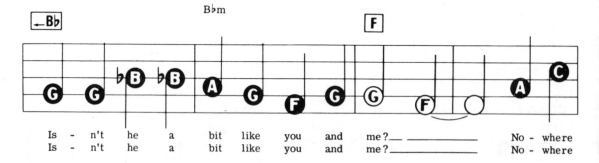

Is - n't he a bit like you and me?__ _____ No - where
Is - n't he a bit like you and me?_____ No - where

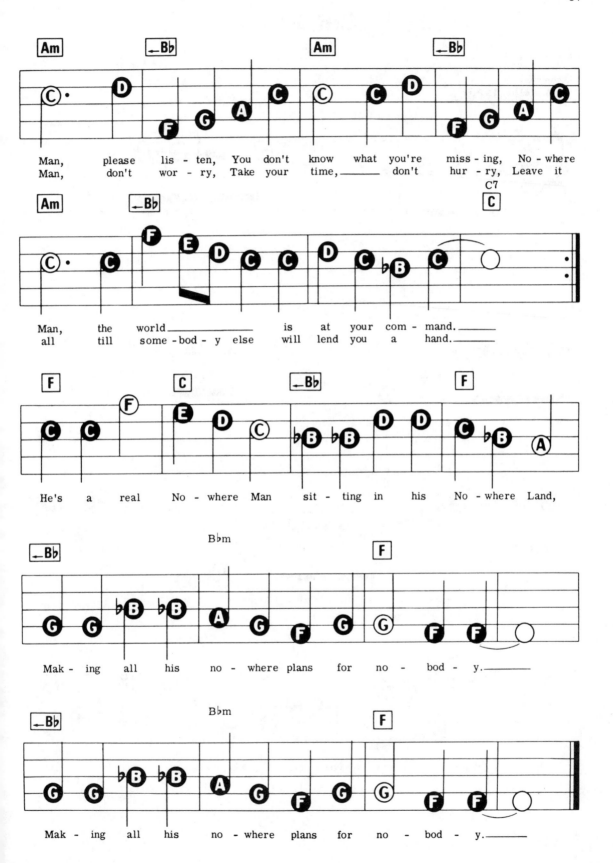

Get Back

Suggested Registration:
  GUITAR or JAZZ ORGAN
Rhythm: ROCK
Tempo: MEDIUM FAST

Words and Music by John Lennon &
Paul McCartney

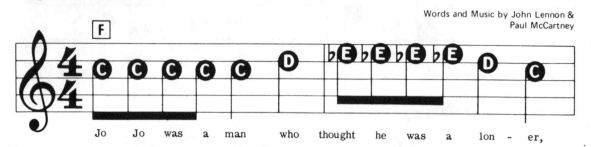

Jo Jo was a man who thought he was a lon - er,

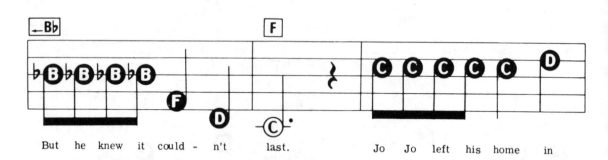

But he knew it could - n't last. Jo Jo left his home in

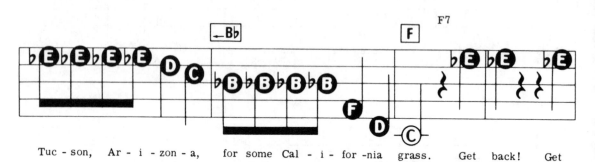

Tuc - son, Ar - i - zon - a, for some Cal - i - for -nia grass. Get back! Get

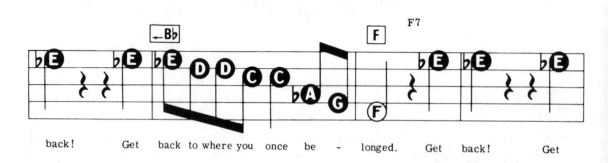

back! Get back to where you once be - longed. Get back! Get

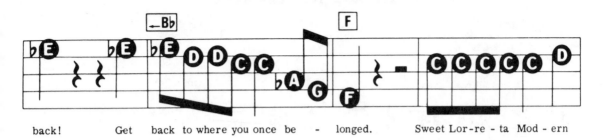

back!   Get   back to where you once be - longed.   Sweet Lor-re - ta Mod - ern

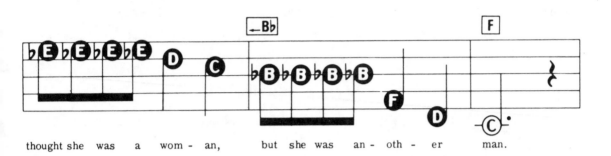

thought she was   a   wom - an,   but she was an - oth - er   man.

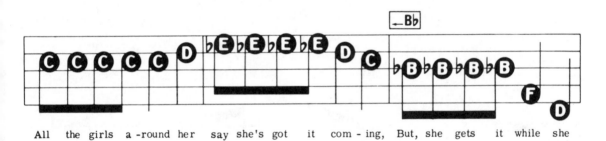

All   the girls a -round her   say she's got   it com - ing, But, she gets   it while she

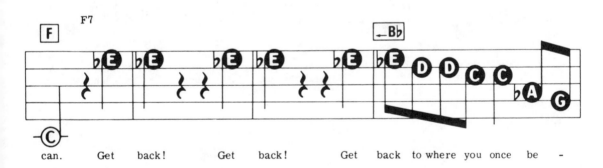

can.   Get   back!   Get   back!   Get   back to where you once be -

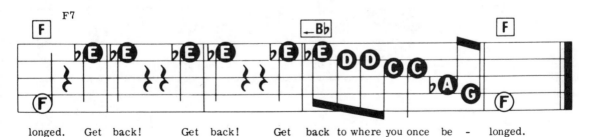

longed.   Get back!   Get   back!   Get back to where you once be - longed.

Eleanor Rigby

Suggested Registration:
    OBOE or JAZZ ORGAN
Rhythm: SOFT ROCK
Tempo: MEDIUM

Words and Music by John Lennon &
Paul McCartney

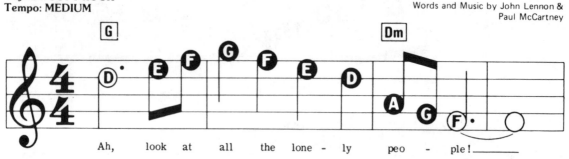

Ah,   look at all the lone - ly peo - ple! _____

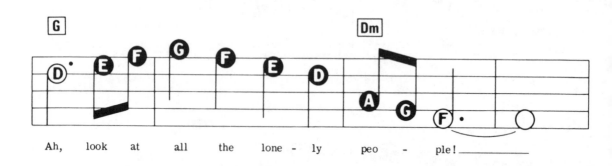

Ah,   look at all the lone - ly peo - ple! _____

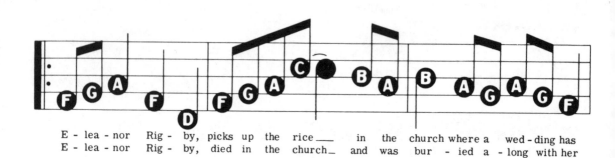

E - lea - nor Rig - by, picks up the rice ____ in the church where a wed - ding has
E - lea - nor Rig - by, died in the church ____ and was bur - ied a - long with her

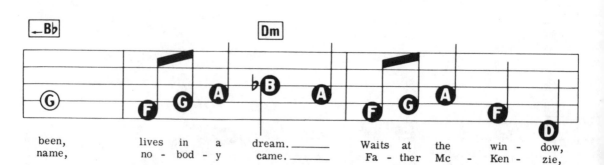

been,   lives in a dream. ____ Waits at the win - dow,
name,   no - bod - y came. ____ Fa - ther Mc - Ken - zie,

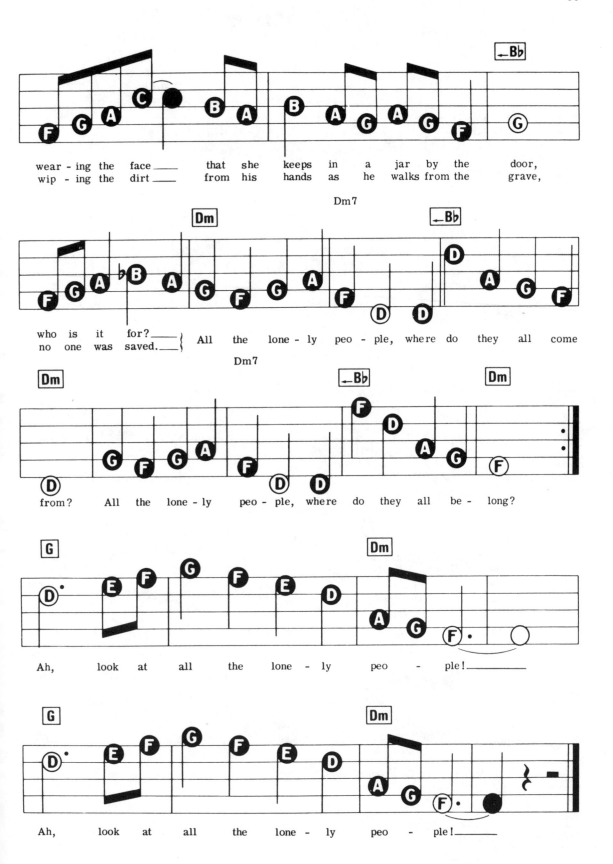

Hey Jude

Suggested Registration:
STRINGS or VIBRAPHONE
Rhythm: **SOFT ROCK**
Tempo: **MEDIUM SLOW**

By John Lennon
and Paul McCartney

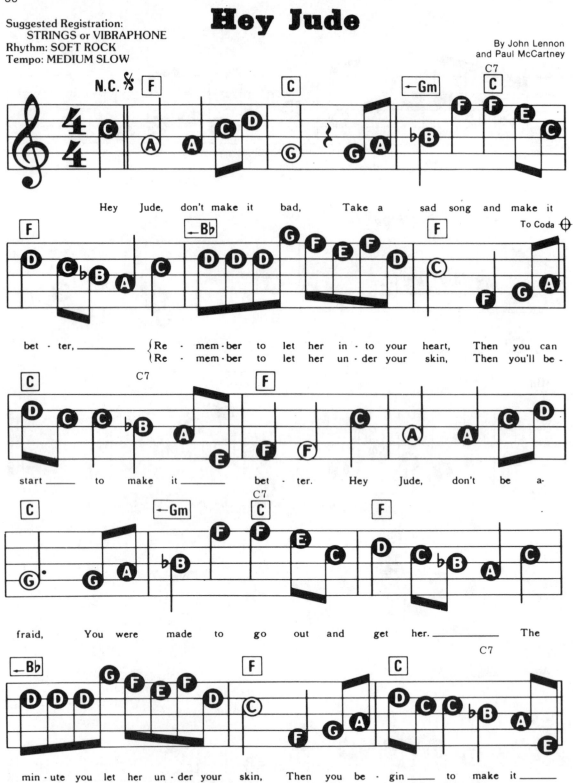

Hey Jude, don't make it bad, Take a sad song and make it

bet-ter, _____ Re-mem-ber to let her in-to your heart, Then you can

Re-mem-ber to let her un-der your skin, Then you'll be-

start _____ to make it _____ bet-ter. Hey Jude, don't be a-

fraid, You were made to go out and get her. _____ The

min-ute you let her un-der your skin, Then you be-gin ___ to make it ___

Michelle

Suggested Registration:
FLUTE or STRINGS
Rhythm: SOFT ROCK
Tempo: MEDIUM

Words and Music by John Lennon &
Paul McCartney

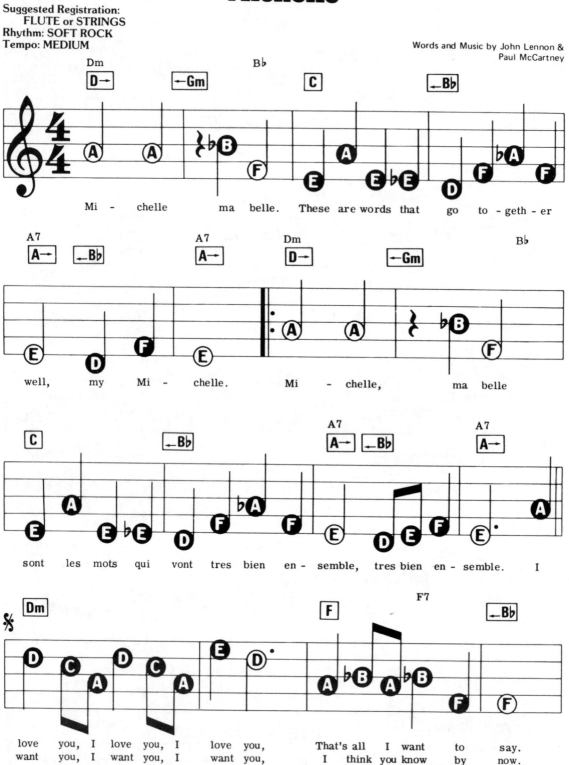

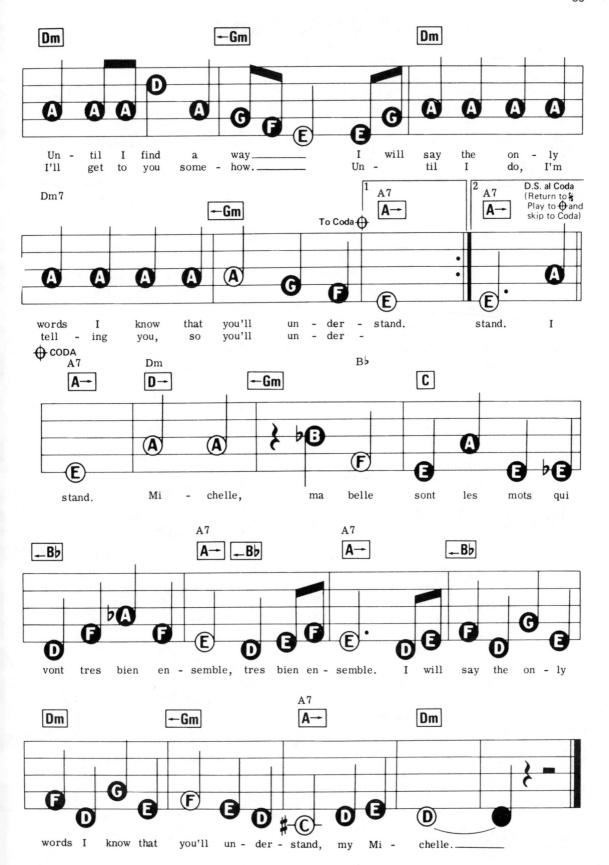

I Feel Fine

Suggested Registration:
GUITAR or JAZZ ORGAN
Rhythm: ROCK
Tempo: MEDIUM FAST

By John Lennon
and Paul McCartney

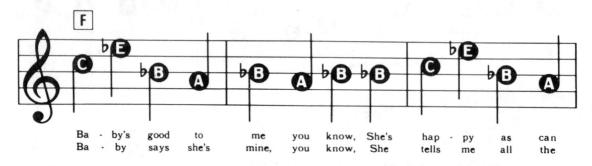

Ba - by's good to me you know, She's hap - py as can
Ba - by says she's mine, you know, She tells me all the

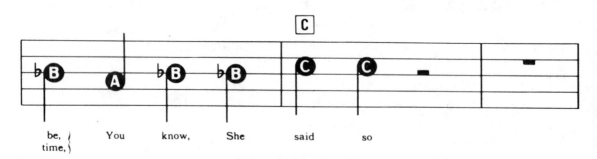

be, You know, She said so
time,

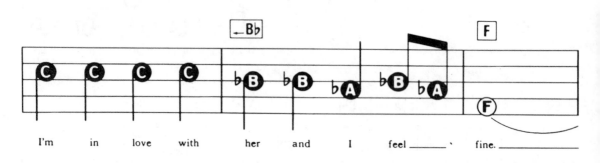

I'm in love with her and I feel _____ fine. _____

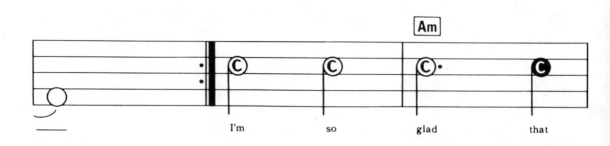

I'm so glad that

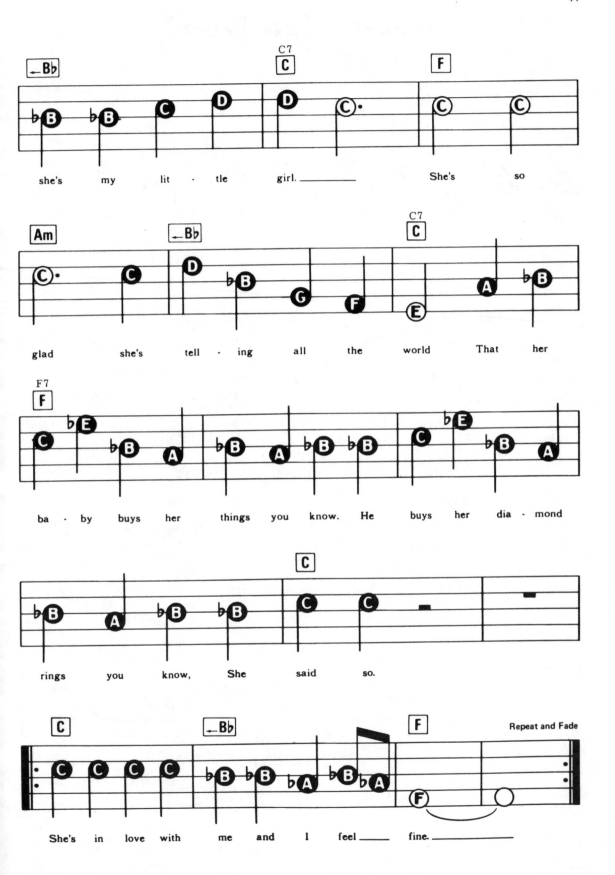

Norwegian Wood

(THIS BIRD HAS FLOWN)

Suggested Registration:
OBOE or STRINGS
Rhythm: WALTZ
Tempo: MEDIUM FAST

By John Lennon
and Paul McCartney

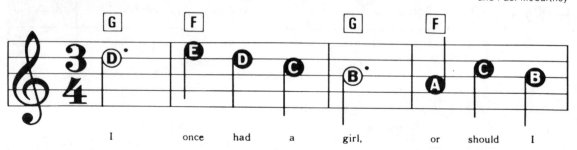

I once had a girl, or should I

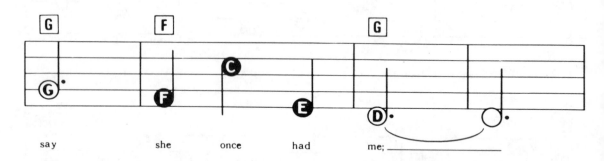

say she once had me;

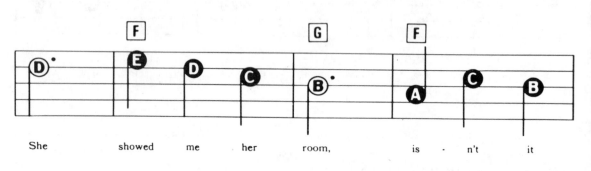

She showed me her room, is - n't it

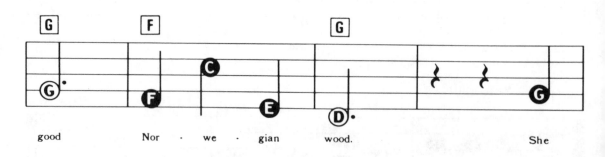

good Nor - we - gian wood. She

44

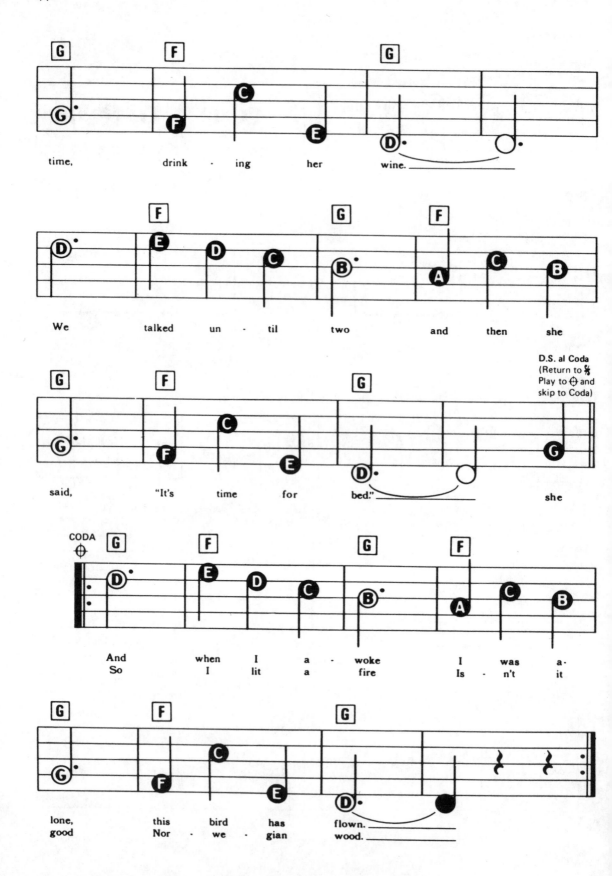

We Can Work It Out

Suggested Registration:
PIANO or JAZZ ORGAN
Rhythm: ROCK
Tempo: MEDIUM

By John Lennon
and Paul McCartney

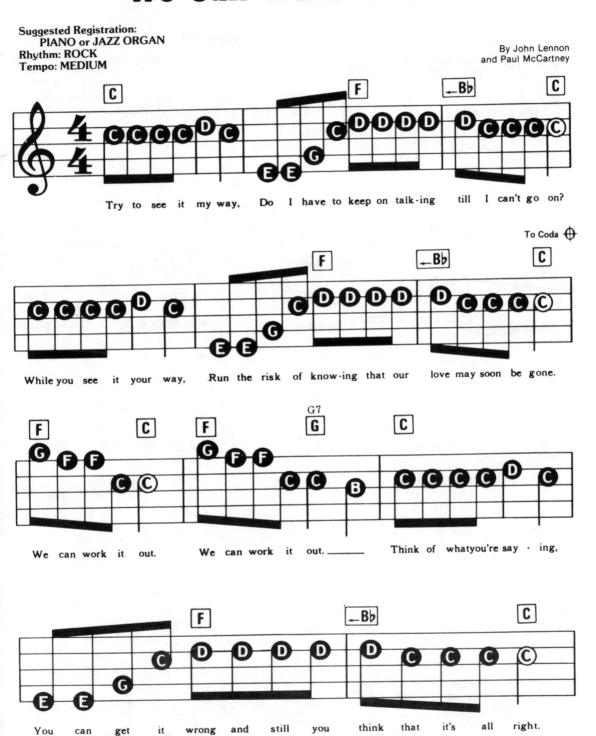

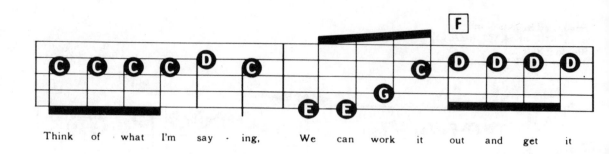

Think of what I'm say - ing, We can work it out and get it

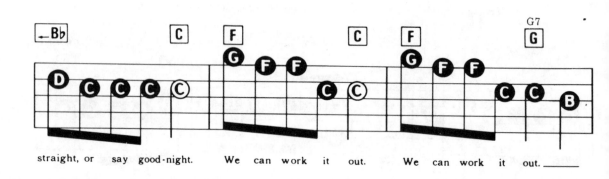

straight, or say good-night. We can work it out. We can work it out. _____

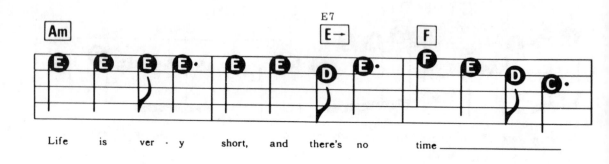

Life is ver - y short, and there's no time _____

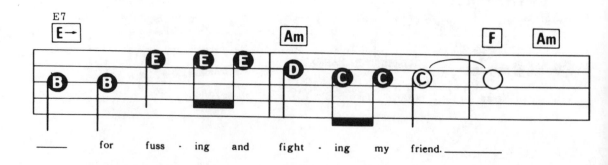

_____ for fuss - ing and fight - ing my friend. _____

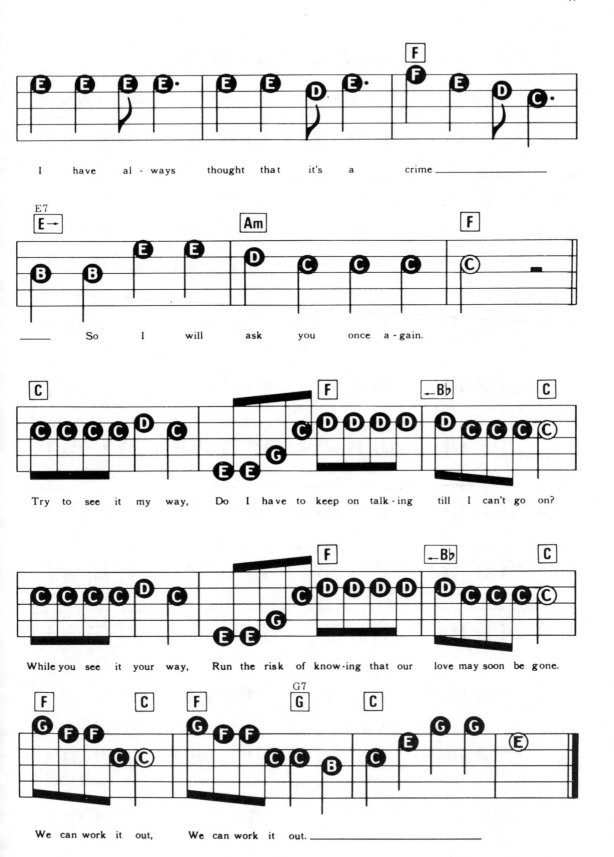

MASTER CHORD CHART

	Major	Minor	Seventh	Minor seventh
C				
C# Db				
D				
Eb				
E				
F				
F# Gb				
G				
Ab				
A				
Bb				
B				

Printed in Great Britain by ETP (E. Anglia) Ltd.

4/97 (27528)